Healthy
Juices
for daily use

TARLA DALAL
India's # 1 Cookery Author

S&C
SANJAY & CO.
MUMBAI

Price: Rs.89/-

Published & Distributed by : **Sanjay & Company**

353/A-1, Shah & Nahar Industrial Estate, Dhanraj Mill Compound, Lower Parel (W), Mumbai - 400 013. INDIA.

Tel. : (91-22) 2496 8068 ● Fax : (91-22) 2496 5876 ● E-mail : sanjay@tarladalal.com

Printed by : **Jupiter Prints**, Mumbai

| **Recipe Research & Production Design** Arati Fedane Umaima Abdulally | **Nutritionist** Nisha Katira Sapna Thakkar | **Photography** Jignesh Jhaveri | **Design** Satyamangal Rege |
| | | **Food Stylist** Shubhangi Dhaimade | **Typesetting** Adityas Enterprises |

DISCLAIMER

While every precaution has been taken in the preparation of this book, the publishers and the author assume no responsibility for errors or omissions. Neither is any liability assumed for damages resulting from the use of information contained herein. And of course, no book is a substitute for a qualified medical advice. So it is wiser to modify your dietary patterns under the supervision of a doctor or a nutritionist.

BULK PURCHASES

Tarla Dalal Cookbooks are ideal gifts. If you are interested in buying more than 500 assorted copies of Tarla Dalal Cookbooks at special prices, please contact us at 91-22-2496 8068 or email : sanjay@tarladalal.com

INTRODUCTION

"Drink your way to good health"

They are often referred to as 'live food'. They fit into our hectic schedules very easily. Made for a healthy lifestyle for people of all ages, they are simple to make and absolutely delicious to taste. We are talking about the wonder food called '**JUICES**'.

In my book titled *'Healthy Juices'*, I have put together a variety of 39 nutrient-packed drinks that you can include in your regular diet. These appetizing juices are made from natural fruits and vegetables and unlike commercially available juices, they do not contain any added sugar, salt, additives or preservatives. These juices are full of vitamins and minerals that will keep you on the go all day long.

The juices here are clubbed under 5 unique sections viz. **Power Juices** (to boost energy and increase stamina), **Cleansing Juices** (to cleanse the system), **Vitality Juices** (to build up the immune system and fight diseases), **Healing Juices** (to combat different ailments like anaemia, hypertension etc.) and **Fresh and Fruity** (a plethora of fresh fruit juices).

Each recipe in this book highlights the nutrients, which the juice is rich in and its importance for our health.

All the recipes in this book will yield up to 300 ml (2 small glasses) of juice. If you desire more servings, double or triple the recipe as required. Also make your own choice for the method of juicing i.e. a Hopper/Juicer or a Mixer/Blender.

Have fun while making the juices, enjoy their taste and live a healthier, happier life!

Regards

Tarla Dalal

CONTENTS

Say Yes to Juices!

Health professionals have always stressed about the advantages of having fresh fruits and vegetables at least 5 to 6 times a day to make up for ones nutrient requirement. But the question that arises is "Does our daily diet encompass so much raw fruits and vegetables?"

A survey, if taken, is sure to prove that most of us skip this necessary food from our diet.

Turn to freshly made juices to consume a healthy portion of vegetables/ fruits daily at one go. For example, one cup of carrot juice is approximately equivalent to four cups of raw chopped carrots. I am sure a glass of juice early in the morning or anytime of the day can easily fit into our busy lifestyles.

Although eating fruits and vegetables in their natural state does provide us with a substantial amount of vitamins and minerals, juicing benefits us equally. It is true that while juicing some amount of fibre is lost due to the straining process. However, the digestive enzymes and the nutrients are retained in the juice, which are easily absorbed by our body.

Remember, despite the fact that juices provide us with a quick and easy way to increase our nutrient intake, do make it a point to include whole fruits, vegetables, whole grains and legumes in your daily diet.

Top 10 Benefits of Juicing

1. Energizing and satiating
2. A chockfull of vitamins, minerals and enzymes (that make food easier to digest)
3. Provides natural sugars

8

4. Quick and easy to prepare
5. Easily absorbed
6. Powerful blood cleanser
7. Detoxifies the body
8. Replaces lost fluids and electrolytes (e.g. sodium and potassium)
9. Concentrated phyto-nutrients and antioxidants that help fight diseases
10. Proven healing properties

Getting Equipped

For successful juicing and blending, you will need some basic equipments. *Along with blender or juicer you will also need other useful equipments like sharp knives, chopping board, peelers, apple corers, etc.*

Blenders are ideal for soft fruits like bananas, chickoos, papayas etc. as they help retain all the fibre if the juice is unstrained. Juicers, on the other hand, are best for firm fruits and vegetables such as apples, carrots etc. but they are not good for soft fruits which clog up the machine and do not provide much juice. Two types of juicers are available in the market. Both are also referred to as **hoppers**. They are:

1) **Centrifugal Juicers:** These work by finely grating vegetables and fruits and spinning them at great speed. This separates the juice from the pulp. They also have a pulp collector where the pulp residue is collected and a spout from which juice comes out.

2) **Masticating Juicers:** These are a little more hi-tech and also more expensive. Instead of shredding the fruits and vegetables, they finely chop it and then force the pulp through a mesh 9

to separate out the juice. These juicers produce a greater volume of juice than centrifugal models and because of the method of extraction; the juice contains more live enzymes.

Your Guide to Juicing at Home

Juicing is indeed a great way to add vegetables and fruits to our diet, which we need for maintaining good health. To most of us though, juicing is a fairly new idea… here are a few points to help all you beginners out.

BEFORE JUICING

1) All fruits and vegetables should be juiced raw. Always choose fruits and vegetables that are ripe but firm. Very ripe fruits may clog the juicer so use a blender instead.

2) Choose only the freshest produce for juicing. Rubbery vegetables, bruised fruits, wilted greens and over or under-ripe fruits will produce juices that are neither tasty nor healthy.

3) Make sure that all the fruits and vegetables are cleaned thoroughly as they are to be consumed raw.

4) For maximum freshness, flavour and nutrients, cut or chop the fruits and vegetables just before you are ready to juice them, as nutrients like vitamin C are lost as soon as the cut fruit is exposed to the atmosphere. Also fruits like apple and banana do oxidize as soon as they are exposed to air.

5) Do not peel or core the fruits and vegetables as most of the fibre lies just beneath the skin. All leafy vegetables (spinach, lettuce, celery etc.), carrots, apples and citrus fruits (outer peel removed) can be easily passed through the juicer. A word of caution here, apple seeds are toxic and hence should be discarded, so should the top and leaves of carrots.

WHILE JUICING

1) You'll need a juice machine (Juicer / Hopper) or a food processor (Mixer / Blender). See section **Getting Equipped, page 9**.

2) Cut the fruits or vegetables into small sized pieces that will fit into the mouth of the juice machine. Turn it on and push the pieces through the mouth of the juicer.

3) Put the ingredients through the juicer in manageable quantities and at a steady pace and alternate them if possible to ensure that the juices mix well. If you push too many pieces of fruit or vegetable in one go, the machine will clog up.

4) Put a hard ingredient like carrot after softer ingredients like celery, parsley etc. This will keep the juice flowing freely and prevent blockages.

AFTER JUICING

1) It is best to drink the juice within 5 minutes of making to avoid the loss of nutrients.

2) While it is definitely best to serve juices when they are just freshly made, you may want to store them for one reason or another. The best option would be to make juicy ice cubes as shown in the section **Serving and Decorating Juices, page 12.**

3) The one and only dreary thing about juicing is cleaning the equipment. It is important that the juicer or blender is cleaned thoroughly (or at least soaked) as soon as the juice is made. If this is not done, the pulp will stick to the grater and it will be really difficult to clean. It would then become a haven for bacteria multiplication and then pollute the juice as well.

Serving and Decorating Juices

There are many attractive and imaginative ways to serve fresh drinks. With a little forethought and creativity, you can present friends and family with gorgeous-looking concoctions.

Garnishing allows you to be inventive, but it is intended for enhancing the flavour, colour and overall appearance of your drink rather than disguising it. Therefore ensure that you do not make your juice look like a fruit salad! Choose a garnishing fruit that complements or reflects the ingredients of the drink. Here are a few ideas...

1) **Adding ice:** Whether crushed or as cubes, ice is a wonderful vehicle for serving, cooling and decorating drinks. Juice can be poured over crushed ice or plain or flavoured ices may be added. Here are a few ways to make flavoured ices:

   a) **Fruit ice-cubes:** Small pieces of fruits, vegetables, berries etc can be put in to ice-trays and water can be poured over it before it is frozen to make fruit ice-cubes.

   b) **Juicy ice-cubes:** Leftover juice can immediately be put into ice-trays and frozen. These ice-cubes can be added to next day's fresh juice to enhance it's aesthetic appeal. This will prevent dilution of the juice and also avoid wastage. On the other hand, lime juice flavoured ice cubes help enhance the vitamin C content of any juice.

2) **Fruit Purée drizzle:** For a striped effect, purée of fruits can be poured down the inside of glasses before adding to the drink.

3) **Edible Stirrers:** Celery and carrot sticks are the most commonly used edible stirrers. Just cut them into sticks a little longer than your glass and place them in the drink. For a more decorative touch, fringe the celery by making long gnashes at one end and placing it in ice-cold water.

12

4) **Fruit Skewers:** Pierce cubes of fruits and vegetables on a toothpick and place horizontally on the juice glass.

5) **Glass Decorations:** Place fruit slices on the rim of a glass or experiment with rind of fruits like oranges, sweet lime, lemons as shown in the pictures.

6) **Other Decorations:** Extravagances such as paper umbrellas, decorative straws etc. are available in the market. They add a flamboyant touch to the drink and can be used for parties and special occasions.

Beat the heat; keep illness at bay and welcome a happier healthier you with these excellent juicing ideas.

POWER JUICES

In today's fast world, everyone needs energy and stamina to cope up with various activities and responsibilities. To make it through the day successfully, we need a solid dose of the right kind of nutrition. This section deals with juices that will keep you going all day, with a smile on your face.

Power juices covers the body's primary needs when it comes to daily activities, exercise and over all health.

The juices under this section are planned using select ingredients and combinations like apple, pineapple, grapes, pear, beetroot all of which are rich in carbohydrates i.e. fructose (the fruit sugar) and essential vitamins and minerals.

Some such power-packed treats are luscious **Instant Energizer**, page 15, to help maintain your energy levels all day long, **Power Beverage**, page 17, ideal for priming your body before a hectic day ahead, **Melon and Papaya Tango**, page 22, an excellent fulfilling breakfast idea. etc.

~ *Instant Energizer* ~

Picture on page 19.

Jam-packed schedule? This is an ideal drink to boost your energy and to keep you on your toes all day.

Makes 2 small glasses (300 ml).

Ingredients
3 medium sized carrots (unpeeled), cut into pieces
1 medium sized apple (unpeeled), cored and cut into pieces
2 to 3 celery sticks, roughly chopped
1 small orange, peeled and separated into segments
crushed ice to serve

Procedure
HOPPER / JUICER

1. Juice all the ingredients.
2. Add some crushed ice in 2 glasses and pour the juice over it.
   Serve immediately.

MIXER / BLENDER

1. Blend all the ingredients using little water (if required) till smooth.
2. Strain the juice using a strainer or a muslin cloth.
3. Add some crushed ice in 2 glasses and pour the juice over it.
   Serve immediately.

....

Nutritive values per glass:
Energy : 160 kcal.
Protein : 2.0 gm.
Carbohydrate : 36.0 gm.
Fat : 0.9 gm.
Vitamin A : 3451.3 mcg.
Vitamin C : 21.8 mg.
Folic Acid : 22.5 mcg.
Fibre : 3.1 gm.

Instant Energizer is super-rich in antioxidants viz. vitamins A and C, folic acid and fibre which protect against heart disease and some cancers. As an added bonus, carotenoids from carrot and apple slow ageing and also protect the skin against sun damage.

~ *Power Beverage* ~

One sniff of this aromatic juice is enough to set the senses in overdrive. Made out of a variety of fruits, it is the perfect way to make your day!

Makes 2 small glasses (300 ml).

Ingredients
2 medium sized pears (unpeeled), cored and cut into pieces
1 medium sized apple (unpeeled), cored and cut into pieces
2 big pineapple slices, with the skin
¼ cup black grapes
crushed ice to serve

Procedure
HOPPER / JUICER

1. Juice all the ingredients.
2. Add some crushed ice in 2 glasses and pour the juice over it. Serve immediately.

MIXER / BLENDER

1. Remove the pineapple skin and blend all the ingredients using little water (if

required) till smooth.
2. Strain the juice using a strainer or a muslin cloth.
3. Add some crushed ice in 2 glasses and pour the juice over it.
   Serve immediately.

....

Nutritive values per glass:
Energy : 175 kcal.
Protein : 1.4 gm.
Carbohydrate : 40.1 gm.
Fat : 0.9 gm.
Calcium : 38.9 mg.
Fibre : 3.2 gm.
Vitamin C : 30.5 mg.

The soluble fibre found in pears and apples (mainly in the skin) together with the rich supply of natural sugars in grapes and natural healing enzyme 'bromelain' in pineapple - aids digestion and also provides instant energy. Vitamin C and flavonoids like 'quercetin' and 'catechins' found in grapes add to its cancer-fighting power.

POWER JUICES : FROM LEFT TO RIGHT
INSTANT ENERGIZER : Recipe on page 15, BEAT TREAT : Recipe on page 20 →
and LEMONY LETTUCE DRINK : Recipe on page 26. → 18

~ *Beet Treat* ~

Picture on page 19.

Kick start your day with this energy boosting treat. Rich in flavour and nutrients, it satisfies aesthetic as well as nutritional demands.

Makes 2 small glasses (300 ml).

Ingredients
4 medium sized carrots (unpeeled), cut into pieces
1 medium sized beetroot (unpeeled), cut into pieces
1 medium sized apple (unpeeled), cored and cut into pieces
crushed ice to serve

Procedure
HOPPER / JUICER

1. Juice all the ingredients.
2. Add some crushed ice in 2 glasses and pour the juice over it. Serve immediately.

MIXER / BLENDER

1. Blend all the ingredients using little water (if required) till smooth.

2. Strain the juice using a strainer or a muslin cloth.
3. Add some crushed ice in 2 glasses and pour the juice over it.
   Serve immediately.

....

Nutritive values per glass:
Energy : 168 kcal.
Protein : 2.7 gm.
Carbohydrate : 37.2 gm.
Fat : 0.9 gm.
Iron : 3.2 mg.
Zinc : 1.2 mg.

The Beet Treat is high in carbohydrates as it contains beetroot, which is the richest source of natural sugars. Apples give this juice good body thus making sure it satiates your appetite. This juice is a healthy accompaniment to any breakfast or snack.

~ *Melon and Papaya Tango* ~

This snazzy orange coloured-carbohydrate rich juice is a fulfilling breakfast idea. Lemon juice makes it more interesting by imparting a tangy flavour.

Makes 2 small glasses (300 ml).

Ingredients

½ small papaya, peeled, deseeded and cut into pieces
1 small muskmelon (kharbooja), peeled and cut into pieces
½ tsp lemon juice
crushed ice to serve

Procedure

HOPPER / JUICER

1. Juice all the ingredients.
2. Add the lemon juice and mix well.
3. Add some crushed ice in 2 glasses and pour the juice over it. Serve immediately.

MIXER / BLENDER

1. Blend all the ingredients using little water (if required) till smooth.
2. Strain the juice using a strainer or a muslin cloth.
3. Add the lemon juice and mix well.
4. Add some crushed ice in 2 glasses and pour the juice over it.
   Serve immediately.

....

Nutritive values per glass:
Energy : 64 kcal.
Protein : 1.2 gm.
Carbohydrate : 13.8 gm.
Fat : 0.5 gm.
Fibre : 1.6 gm.
Vitamin A : 995.1 mcg.

Papaya helps to maintain blood glucose levels. As there is a steady supply of glucose, you feel energetic throughout the day. It also has a laxative effect thus helping to relieve constipation. As a an added benefit, melons contain a substance "adenosine" that makes blood less sticky, thus reducing the risk of blood clots and heart attack. Because of its high vitamin content this tango is a boost to the immune system as well.

~ *Spinach Spectacular* ~

Popeye munched on spinach for strength, you can do just that... or drink a glassful of this spectacular juice to keep you going full force all day!

Makes 2 small glasses (300 ml).

Ingredients
1 big apple (unpeeled), cored and cut into pieces
10 to 12 spinach (palak) leaves, roughly chopped
2 big pineapple slices, with the skin
1 to 2 celery sticks with the leaves, finely chopped and crushed ice to serve

Procedure
HOPPER / JUICER

1. Juice all the ingredients.
2. Add chopped celery and some crushed ice in 2 glasses and pour the juice over it. Serve immediately.

MIXER / BLENDER

1. Blend all the ingredients using little water (if required) till smooth.
2. Strain the juice using a strainer or a muslin cloth.
3. Add chopped celery and some crushed ice in 2 glasses and pour the juice over it. Serve immediately.

....

Nutritive values per glass:
Energy : 114 kcal.
Protein : 0.9 gm.
Carbohydrate : 25.6 gm.
Fat : 0.8 gm.
Iron : 3.1 mg.
Vitamin A : 993.3 mcg.
Folic Acid : 20.9 mcg.

Pineapple is the source of carbohydrate here to provide energy. Taken with a light lunch, it will see you through a mentally or physically tiring afternoon and still leave you with energy reserves for the rest of the day. Also, if you are really tired, celery in this juice has a restful and calming effect. Chopped celery gives it a crunchy bite and also enhances its appearance.

~ *Lemony Lettuce Drink* ~

Picture on page 19.

Lettuce is not just a salad food! Combined with lemon, this delightful juice is just the thing to revive you from that sinking feeling!

Makes 2 small glasses (300 ml).

Ingredients
1 medium sized apple (unpeeled), cored and cut into pieces
1 medium sized orange, peeled and separated into segments
2 to 3 lettuce leaves (preferably iceberg), roughly chopped
1 tsp lemon juice
½ tsp black salt (sanchal) (optional)
crushed ice to serve

Procedure
HOPPER / JUICER

1. Juice all the ingredients.
2. Add the lemon juice and black salt and mix well.
3. Add some crushed ice in 2 glasses and pour the juice over it. Serve immediately.

MIXER / BLENDER

1. Blend all the ingredients using little water (if required) till smooth.
2. Strain the juice using a strainer or a muslin cloth.
3. Add the lemon juice and black salt and mix well.
4. Add some crushed ice in 2 glasses and pour the juice over it. Serve immediately.

....

Nutritive values per glass:
Energy : 91 kcal.
Protein : 0.9 gm.
Carbohydrate : 20.4 gm.
Fat : 0.7 gm.
Vitamin C : 19.2 mg.
Calcium : 32.3 mg.
Fibre : 1.3 gm.

Try this unusual combination of fruits and vegetables for some real health power with a vitamin C and calcium boost in a glass. There are many types of lettuce available. Dark green varieties lend a slightly bitter taste to juices, so use only the lighter green variety of lettuce. It is easier to juice firm rather than softer leaves.

CLEANSING JUICES

Pollution, toxic wastes, chemically treated and processed foods tax our body with too many harmful substances. These speed up the ageing process and can also be carcinogenic (cancer causing). Also the fact that we end up eating a lot of junk food adds to the collective effect.

All this toxin build-up makes a cleansing regime a must for our bodies.

A classic **"cleansing diet"** is the one that allows the body to rid itself of chemicals and other toxins so it can function smoothly. Place your bet on freshly made juices, as they are a storehouse of antioxidants that also aid keeping diseases at bay. Natural fruit and vegetable juices, with their gentle powers i.e. nutrients like fibre, water, digestive enzymes, vitamin C etc. regenerate the glands and organs associated with digestion. This helps improve muscular action to sweep off the toxins and increase body's ability to absorb nutrients.

Juices in this section are planned with choice fruits and vegetables that improve the efficiency of our body's natural "Cleansing System". The juice of citrus fruits like **oranges, sweet lime** etc. stimulates salivary glands that aid digestion. Herbs and spices like **parsley, celery and ginger** increase the production of stomach's digestive juices to ensure proper breakdown of food and availability of vitamins and minerals. **Orange, cucumber and watermelon** are used as their high water content act as a cleanser by eliminating the waste from our body.

To let these juices work at their best, do remember to avoid overeating and consuming junk foods as these are loaded with high fat and low in fibre which would make digestion more difficult.

A few suggested juices in this section are **Minty Morning,** page 29, **Ginger Spice,** page 35, **Cucumber Cooler,** page 38 etc.

~ Minty Morning ~

Picture on page 37.

This is a variation of the most popular breakfast juice of all time, the orange juice. It is sure to appeal to everyone's taste buds as well as health.

Makes 2 small glasses (300 ml).

Ingredients
4 medium sized oranges, peeled and separated into segments
8 to 10 sprigs of mint (phudina) with the leaves, roughly chopped
crushed ice to serve

Procedure
HOPPER / JUICER

1. Juice all the ingredients.
2. Add some crushed ice in 2 glasses and pour the juice over it. Serve immediately.

MIXER / BLENDER

1. Blend all the ingredients using little water (if required) till smooth.
2. Strain the juice using a strainer or a muslin cloth.

3. Add some crushed ice in 2 glasses and pour the juice over it. Serve immediately.

....

Nutritive values per glass:
Energy : 105 kcal.
Protein : 1.8 gm.
Carbohydrate : 23.5 gm.
Fat : 0.5 gm.
Iron : 1.8 mg.
Fibre : 1.0 gm.

Oranges boost overall resistance and also stimulate the salivary glands thus aiding digestion. Mint on the other hand is rich in iron and vitamin C. It is also the best digestive and cooling herb. By combining the health-giving properties of oranges with mint; this juice makes for a powerful cleanser.

~ *Melon Punch* ~

Picture on page 37.

Here's a happy green coloured cleansing drink that will protect your skin from the harmful toxins and make it glow!

Makes 2 small glasses (300 ml).

Ingredients
½ green melon (hara kharbooja), peeled and cut into pieces
2 to 3 sprigs of coriander, roughly chopped
½ cup green grapes
crushed ice to serve

Procedure
HOPPER / JUICER

1. Juice all the ingredients.
2. Add some crushed ice in 2 glasses and pour the juice over it. Serve immediately.

MIXER / BLENDER

1. Blend all the ingredients using little water (if required) till smooth.

2. Strain the juice using a strainer or a muslin cloth.
3. Add some crushed ice in 2 glasses and pour the juice over it. Serve immediately.

....

Nutritive values per glass:
Energy : 42 kcal.
Protein : 0.6 gm.
Carbohydrate : 9.1 gm.
Fat : 0.3 gm.
Fibre : 1.4 gm.
Potassium : 309.9 mg.

Melons have high content of water and thus act as diuretic hydrating our body and eliminating toxins from our body. Besides melon's diuretic and cleansing power, its seeds are just as good. Rich in potassium, which helps to lower high blood pressure, they are also valued for their zinc and vitamin E content. So do not forget to add a few.

~ Rainbow Cocktail ~

Picture on page 37.

Luscious oranges when blended with zesty sweetlime and tangy black grapes make a favourite anytime drink. Serve it with a hint of black salt for that added zing!

Makes 2 small glasses (300 ml).

Ingredients

2 big oranges, peeled and separated into segments
1 medium sized sweetlime, peeled and separated into segments
¼ cup black grapes
1 tbsp lemon juice
½ tsp black salt (sanchal)
crushed ice to serve

Procedure

HOPPER / JUICER

1. Juice all the ingredients.
2. Add the lemon juice and black salt and mix well.
3. Add some crushed ice in 2 glasses and pour the juice over it. Serve immediately.

MIXER / BLENDER

1. Blend all the ingredients using little water (if required) till smooth.
2. Strain the juice using a strainer or a muslin cloth.
3. Add the lemon juice and black salt and mix well.
4. Add some crushed ice in 2 glasses and pour the juice over it. Serve immediately.

....

Nutritive values per glass:
Energy : 111 kcal.
Protein : 1.6 gm.
Carbohydrate : 25.0 gm.
Fat : 0.6 gm.
Vitamin A : 1656.0 mcg.
Fibre : 1.4 gm.

Important part of our daily diet is fluids. When taken in any form, plain water or juices they not only cleanse our body but also nourish it. Orange and sweetlime being juicy citrus fruits work well as diuretics and can be easily fitted into our daily health regime. Dark-skinned grapes are rich in fibre and antioxidants (vitamin A), which fight against degenerative diseases like cancer, ageing etc. Besides tasting being sumptuous, it is a liver and intestinal cleanser too.

~ *Ginger Spice* ~

Picture on page 1.

Ginger is a warming spice that naturally lends itself to both fruit and vegetable juices, complementing citrus fruits particularly well.

Makes 2 small glasses (300 ml).

Ingredients
2 medium sized carrots (unpeeled), cut into pieces
1 apple (unpeeled), cored and cut into pieces
1 medium sized orange, peeled and separated into segments
12 mm. (½") piece ginger
crushed ice to serve

Procedure
HOPPER / JUICER

1. Juice all the ingredients.
2. Add some crushed ice in 2 glasses and pour the juice over it. Serve immediately.

MIXER / BLENDER
1. Blend all the ingredients using little water (if required) till smooth.
2. Strain the juice using a strainer or a muslin cloth.
3. Add some crushed ice in 2 glasses and pour the juice over it. Serve immediately.

....

Nutritive values per glass:
Energy : 126 kcal.
Protein : 1.5 gm.
Carbohydrate : 28.4 gm.
Fat : 0.8 gm.
Vitamin C : 19.8 mg.
Fibre : 2.3 gm.

This cleansing juice has powerful antiseptic and anti-inflammatory benefits. Ginger Spice is a gentle cleanser, which benefits from the powerful volatile oils present in the ginger, as well as from the cleansing and digestive benefits of carrot, apple and orange.

CLEANSING JUICES : FROM LEFT TO RIGHT
MELON PUNCH : Recipe on page 31, RAINBOW COCKTAIL : Recipe on page 33 →
and MINTY MORNING : Recipe on page 29. → 36

~ *Cucumber Cooler* ~

Picture on page 1.

You simply must try this unusual combination! Add ripe melon for maximum sweetness.

Makes 2 small glasses (300 ml).

Ingredients
½ small musk melon (kharbooja), peeled, deseeded and cut into pieces
1 medium sized cucumber (unpeeled), cut into pieces
crushed ice to serve

Procedure
HOPPER / JUICER

1. Juice all the ingredients.
2. Add some crushed ice in 2 glasses and pour the juice over it. Serve immediately.

MIXER / BLENDER

1. Blend all the ingredients using little water (if required) till smooth.
2. Strain the juice using a strainer or a muslin cloth.

3. Add some crushed ice in 2 glasses and pour the juice over it. Serve immediately.

....

Nutritive values per glass:

Energy : 22 kcal.

Protein : 0.5 gm.

Carbohydrate : 4.4 gm.

Fat : 0.2 gm.

Calcium : 33.2 mg.

Vitamin A : 147.9 mcg.

Vitamin C : 26.4 mg.

Cucumber, being full of water has a strong diuretic action and thus helps to remove toxins from the body which otherwise accumulate in our body and cause skin problems like pimples and other bodily functions.

To add to this, it is also a storehouse of important minerals such as calcium and zinc, alongside other nutrients like folic acid, vitamin A and C.

~ *Papaya Coconut Drink* ~

This drink shares it's colour with the sun during twilight which is a a delight to the eye and the taste buds!

Makes 2 small glasses (300 ml).

Ingredients
2 small tender coconuts (coconut water)
1 cup fresh coconut cream (nariyal ki malai)
2 big slice papaya slices, peeled
crushed ice to serve

Procedure
MIXER / BLENDER
1. Blend all the ingredients till smooth.
2. Add some crushed ice in 2 glasses pour the juice over it. Serve immediately.

Handy tip : Please note that papaya coconut drink cannot be made in the hopper / juicer. This is because the texture of both coconut cream and papaya is soft and hence the hopper/juicer would get clogged.

Nutritive values per glass:
Energy : 78 kcal.
Protein : 2.1 gm.
Carbohydrate : 14.6 gm.
Fat : 1.4 gm.
Potassium : 416.4 mg.
Fibre : 2.1 gm.

Coconut water is an age-old remedy to beat the heat and cool your body. It is also an excellent source of potassium that is required for maintaining the water balance in our body as well as for normal functioning of the heart. Fibre from papaya works at its best when fluid is made available as it absorbs the water and swells, which eases bowel movements and thus keeps our body away from unwanted toxins.

VITALITY JUICES

Our average life might be as long as our ancestors but unlike them, we have to deal with ailments like persistent cold, cough and fever, cancer, heart diseases, hypertension etc. **To give your body's immune system a boost so as to keep you away from these diseases, turn to Vitality Juices.**

Vitality is achieved through the myriad of essential vitamins and minerals present in fruits and vegetables in their natural state. When we switch over to these natural foods, they help our body to defend, repair and restore health. This boost of life leaves you feeling healthier.

Keeping this in mind, we planned recipes with the ingredients that contain powerful antioxidants that give added strength to our immune system and help retain the body's vitality. Juices like **Apple Magic**, page 47 and **Clean Sweep**, page 49, in this section are simply bursting with vitamin C that enhances the immune power to fight against common diseases like cold, cough and fever.

And then there are some other juices that are rich in substances that give us a healthy touch. Examples of such juices are **Ginger Melon Juice**, page 45, which prevents heart diseases, **Pear and Apple Drink**, page 51, which relieves constipation and avoid skin problems like pimple and acne and **Brain Booster**, page 53, which gears up mental aptitude and concentration.

~ *Oriental Magic* ~

Picture on page 55.

The contrasting flavours of pineapple and ginger, along with the protective plant chemicals found in coriander, give this juice a surprising yet delicious flavour.

Makes 2 small glasses (300 ml).

Ingredients
½ medium sized pineapple with the skin, cut into pieces
10 to 15 coriander sprigs with the leaves, roughly chopped
12 mm. (½") piece ginger
crushed ice to serve

Procedure
HOPPER / JUICER

1. Juice all the ingredients.
2. Add some crushed ice in 2 glasses and pour the juice over it. Serve immediately.

MIXER / BLENDER
1. Blend all the ingredients using little water (if required) till smooth.
2. Strain the juice using a strainer or a muslin cloth.
3. Add some crushed ice in 2 glasses and pour the juice over it. Serve immediately.

....

Nutritive values per glass:
Energy : 75 kcal.
Protein : 1.0 gm.
Carbohydrate : 17.3 gm.
Fat : 0.2 gm.
Iron : 3.9 mg.
Vitamin A : 754.1 mcg.

Pineapple is a rich source of iron, which is so essential for maintaining the normal blood circulation and supplying oxygen to our cells. It helps to increase the body's vitality and prevent anaemia. Always select fresh pineapple that is slightly soft to touch, smells delicious and has a good colour with no green patches.

~ Ginger Melon Juice ~

Picture on page 55.

This lovely red coloured juice has its own taste and flavour.... thanks to the unique taste of ginger. It is a sure shot winner with one and all!

Makes 2 small glasses (300 ml).

Ingredients
3 big watermelon slices with the seeds, cut into pieces
12 mm. (½") piece of ginger
crushed ice to serve

Procedure
HOPPER / JUICER

1. Juice all the ingredients.
2. Add some crushed ice in 2 glasses and pour the juice over it. Serve immediately.

MIXER / BLENDER

1. Blend all the ingredients using little water (if required) till smooth.
2. Strain the juice using a strainer or a muslin cloth.
3. Add some crushed ice in 2 glasses and pour the juice over it. Serve immediately.

Nutritive values per glass:

Energy : 26 kcal.
Protein : 0.3 gm.
Carbohydrate : 5.3 gm.
Fat : 0.3 gm.
Iron : 10.6 mg.

Watermelon, a vital fruit loaded with iron and is also an effective diuretic. Besides having the goodness of watermelon, this vitality juice also contains the miraculous power of 'gingerol', a substance present in ginger that dilates blood vessels and improves blood circulation.

~ Apple Magic ~

"An apple a day keeps the doctor away", says the proverb and it's almost true. A dash of lime cuts through the sweetness perfectly and zips up the flavour.

Makes 2 small glasses (300 ml).

Ingredients
4 medium sized apples (unpeeled), cored and cut into pieces
1 tbsp lemon juice
crushed ice to serve

Procedure
HOPPER / JUICER

1. Juice the apple pieces.
2. Add the lemon juice and mix well.
3. Add some crushed ice in 2 glasses and pour the juice over it. Serve immediately.

MIXER / BLENDER

1. Blend the apple pieces using little water (if required) till smooth.

2. Strain the juice using a strainer or a muslin cloth.
3. Add the lemon juice and mix well.
4. Add some crushed ice in 2 glasses and pour the juice over it. Serve immediately.

....

Nutritive values per glass:
Energy : 252 kcal.
Protein : 1.0 gm.
Carbohydrate : 57.1 gm.
Fat : 2.2 gm.
Vitamin C : 7.1 mg.
Fibre : 4.3 gm.

Apples are rich in vitamin C, so they help to boost the immune system and stave off winter colds and flu. Apples contain an enzyme called 'polyphenolase', which when comes in contact with oxygen produces coloured phenolic compounds that impart undesirable brown colour to the pieces. To prevent this, cut the apples just before juicing or simply squeeze lemon juice over the pieces.

~ *Clean Sweep* ~

Celery and parsley make for an exotic combination that takes the not-so-interesting carrot juice up several notches in the favourite list.

Makes 2 small glasses (300 ml).

Ingredients
4 medium sized carrots (unpeeled), cut into pieces
2 to 4 celery sticks with the leaves, roughly chopped
4 to 6 parsley stems with the leaves, roughly chopped
crushed ice to serve

Procedure
HOPPER / JUICER

1. Juice all the ingredients.
2. Add some crushed ice in 2 glasses and pour the juice over it. Serve immediately.

MIXER / BLENDER

1. Blend all the ingredients using little water (if required) till smooth.

49

2. Strain the juice using a strainer or a muslin cloth.
3. Add some crushed ice in 2 glasses and pour the juice over it. Serve immediately.

....

Nutritive values per glass:
Energy : 98 kcal.
Protein : 1.9 gm.
Carbohydrate : 21.7 gm.
Fat : 0.4 gm.
Vitamin C : 13.9 mg.
Folic Acid : 37.3 mcg.

This simple blend makes a great energy and immune booster. Carrot juice has always been refreshing and cooling. Just a touch of parsley to this juice adds enough vitamin C and folic acid to your diet. The high water content in celery makes it ideal for vegetable juicing.

~ *Pear and Apple Drink* ~

Pears have an aromatic scent and delicate flavour, which comes out particularly well when they are juiced.

Makes 2 small glasses (300 ml).

Ingredients
2 medium sized apples (unpeeled), cored and cut into pieces
2 small pears (unpeeled), cored and cut into pieces
4 to 5 sprigs of mint (phudina) with the leaves, roughly chopped
1 medium sized carrot (unpeeled), cut into pieces
crushed ice to serve

Procedure
HOPPER / JUICER

1. Juice all the ingredients.
2. Add some crushed ice in 2 glasses and pour the juice over it. Serve immediately.

MIXER / BLENDER

1. Blend all the ingredients using little water (if required) till smooth.
2. Strain the juice using a strainer or a muslin cloth.
3. Add some crushed ice in 2 glasses and pour the juice over it. Serve immediately.

....

Nutritive values per glass:
Energy : 207 kcal.
Protein : 1.7 gm.
Carbohydrate : 46.8 gm.
Fat : 1.4 gm.
Vitamin C : 4.7 mg.
Vitamin A : 1040.6 mcg.
Fibre : 3.9 gm.

Pears are another detoxifying fruit, which also provides an energizing boost. When the toxins are not eliminated from the body they accumulate in the system and cause digestive problems that further invite skin problems and disturb other bodily functions. Apples are a good all-round fruit, when blended with pears, carrot and mint; they may help in the treatment of constipation.

~ Brain Booster ~

Picture on page 55.

This juice is perfect for the times when you need to concentrate. This brain-booster will keep your mental faculties in top gear!

Makes 2 small glasses (300 ml).

Ingredients

3 medium sized carrots (unpeeled), cut into pieces
1 medium sized apple (unpeeled), cored and cut into pieces
6 to 8 spinach (palak) leaves, roughly chopped
½ medium sized beetroot (unpeeled), cut into pieces
crushed ice to serve

Procedure

HOPPER / JUICER

1. Juice all the ingredients.
2. Add some crushed ice in 2 glasses and pour the juice over it. Serve immediately.

MIXER / BLENDER

1. Blend all the ingredients using little water (if required) till smooth.
2. Strain the juice using a strainer or a muslin cloth.
3. Add some crushed ice in 2 glasses and pour the juice over it. Serve immediately.

....

Nutritive values per glass:
Energy : 148 kcal.
Protein : 2.2 gm.
Carbohydrate : 32.5 gm.
Fat : 0.9 gm.
Iron : 2.7 mg.
Folic Acid : 36.6 mcg.
Zinc : 0.9 mg.

Beetroots, carrots and spinach contain iron, folic acid and zinc, all of which improve the oxygen-carrying power of blood and thereby increase brainpower, concentration and memory. An all-in-one great drink to increase your vitality.

VITALITY JUICES : FROM LEFT TO RIGHT
GINGER MELON JUICE : Recipe on page 45, ORIENTAL MAGIC : Recipe on page 43 →
and BRAIN BOOSTER : Recipe on page 53. → 54

HEALING JUICES

'**Nourish your body well and it will serve you well**', this saying is absolutely true. Just a pint of fresh fruit or vegetable juice is enough to safeguard you against illness and premature ageing.

All of us know that fruits and vegetables are very nutritious, but very few of us are aware of their powerful protective constituents. Natural plant substances present in them play a major part in the protective action against diseases and they do so in a variety of ways.

This section is a compilation of juices as **premier healing juices** for various ailments. Here we have tried to provide cures in a natural way to 8 common ailments like Ageing, Anaemia, High Cholesterol, Diabetes, Hypertension, Indigestion, Osteoporosis and Stress.

Examples of these Juices are **Fresh Complexion Express,** page 57, when taken on a regular basis delays the unwanted process of ageing while the **Anti Cholesterol Shake,** page 68, lowers the cholesterol levels, **Calcium Booster,** page 83, is sure to do wonders for osteoporosis and stress can be well handled by **Super 7 Stress Reliever,** page 88.

Whip up a glassful of life with the help of this section! However, remember that healing juicing are not intended to take the place of a balanced healthy meal and it should always be an addition to your health routine.

~ *Fresh Complexion Express* ~

Here's a vitamin C and iron rich express to prevent the skin from drying out and to reduce facial lines.

Makes 2 small glasses (300 ml).

Ingredients

2 big pineapple slices with the skin, cut into pieces
1 medium sized cucumber (unpeeled), cut into pieces
½ medium sized apple (unpeeled), cored and cut into pieces
crushed ice to serve

Procedure

HOPPER / JUICER

1. Juice all the ingredients.
2. Add some crushed ice in 2 glasses and pour the juice over it. Serve immediately.

MIXER / BLENDER

1. Blend all the ingredients using little water (if required) till smooth.
2. Strain the juice using a strainer or a muslin cloth.
3. Add some crushed ice in 2 glasses and pour the juice over it. Serve immediately.

....

Nutritive values per glass:
Energy : 72 kcal.
Protein : 0.6 gm.
Carbohydrate : 16.4 gm.
Fat : 0.4 gm.
Vitamin C : 33.4 mg.
Iron : 2.5 mg.

Vitamin C, in conjunction with protein, is necessary for the production of collagen - the glue that holds our skin together and circumvents sags or wrinkles. It regulates sebaceous (oil producing) glands to keep skin from drying out; helps prevent facial lines and wrinkles. This may explain why people who consume healthy amounts of vitamin C containing foods have a fresh complexion and a healthy state of mind.

~ Veggie Fruit Cocktail ~

Enjoy radiant skin and an instant energy boost with this fusion of veggies and fruits.

Makes 2 small glasses (300 ml).

Ingredients
1 big apple (unpeeled), cored and cut into pieces
3 medium sized carrots (unpeeled), cut into pieces
½ cup black grapes
12 to 15 spinach (palak) leaves, roughly chopped
2 tsp lemon juice
crushed ice to serve

Procedure
HOPPER / JUICER

1. Juice all the ingredients.
2. Add the lemon juice and mix well.
3. Add some crushed ice in 2 glasses and pour the juice over it. Serve immediately.

MIXER / BLENDER

1. Blend all the ingredients using little water (if required) till smooth.
2. Strain the juice using a strainer or a muslin cloth.
3. Add the lemon juice and mix well.
4. Add some crushed ice in 2 glasses and pour the juice over it. Serve immediately.

....

Nutritive values per glass:
Energy : 179 kcal.
Protein : 2.3 gm.
Carbohydrate : 39.6 gm.
Fat : 1.2 gm.
Vitamin E : 1.0 mg.
Folic Acid : 53.9 mcg.
Zinc : 0.9 mg.

Vitamin E from spinach, vitamin A (carotenoids) from carrots and other antioxidants from grapes and apple all contribute to the goodness of this cocktail. Antioxidants wipe off the free radicals that fasten the ageing process, wrinkles and loosen our skin. Folic acid and zinc are required to maintain normal blood flow to the skin to keep it healthy.

Anaemia

~ *Iron Relish* ~

Picture on page 65.

Iron being needed to make blood and deliver oxygen to the cells, its deficiency results in lethargy and slowed mental function. This juice is apt to keep anaemia at bay.

Makes 2 small glasses (300 ml).

Ingredients
1 big apple (unpeeled), cored and cut into pieces
1 medium sized orange, peeled and separated into segments
6 to 7 spinach (palak) leaves, roughly chopped
½ small beetroot (unpeeled), cut into pieces
crushed ice to serve

Procedure
HOPPER / JUICER

1. Juice all the ingredients.
2. Add some crushed ice in 2 glasses and pour the juice over it. Serve immediately.

MIXER / BLENDER

1. Blend all the ingredients using little water (if required) till smooth.
2. Strain the juice using a strainer or a muslin cloth.
3. Add some crushed ice in 2 glasses and pour the juice over it. Serve immediately.

....

Nutritive values per glass:
Energy : 106 kcal.
Protein : 1.0 gm.
Carbohydrate : 23.7 gm.
Fat : 0.8 gm.
Iron : 1.2 mg.
Vitamin C : 20.9 mg.

It has the goodness of spinach, beetroot, apple and orange. Spinach and beetroot act as iron builders whereas apples impart little sweetness. Oranges are added to benefit from its high vitamin C content, which in turn has a helping hand in enhancing the absorption of iron.

~ Tomato Apple Juice ~

Picture on page 65.

This vibrantly coloured, delicious tangy juice is an excellent nutrient boost to combat anaemia. This juice is sure to gather praises for you!

Makes 2 small glasses (300 ml).

Ingredients
2 medium sized tomatoes, cut into pieces
1 big apple (unpeeled), cored and cut into pieces
crushed ice to serve

Procedure
HOPPER / JUICER

1. Juice all the ingredients.
2. Add some crushed ice in 2 glasses and pour the juice over it. Serve immediately.

MIXER / BLENDER

1. Blend all the ingredients using little water (if required) till smooth.
2. Strain the juice using a strainer or a muslin cloth.

63

3. Add some crushed ice in 2 glasses and pour the juice over it. Serve immediately.

....

Nutritive values per glass:
Energy : 90 kcal.
Protein : 1.0 gm.
Carbohydrate : 19.6 gm.
Fat : 0.8 gm.
Iron : 1.3 mg.
Vitamin C : 22.9 mg.
Folic Acid : 24.0 mcg.

There are many causes of anaemia, iron deficiency being the common one. Other deficiencies include those of folic acid and vitamin B_{12}. Tomatoes, an all-in-one vegetable that is rich in folic acid, iron and vitamin C along with the ever reliable apple makes one fantastic nutrient rich juice.

For Anaemia : FROM LEFT TO RIGHT
IRON RELISH : Recipe on page 61 and TOMATO APPLE JUICE : Recipe on page 63.

~ *Ginger Hopper* ~

Carrots and apples flavoured with ginger makes a juice with a difference. A glass a day each morning will keep heart problems at bay.

Makes 2 small glasses (300 ml).

Ingredients
4 medium sized carrots (unpeeled), cut into pieces
1 medium sized apple (unpeeled), cored and cut into pieces
12 mm. (1") piece of ginger
crushed ice to serve

Procedure
HOPPER / JUICER

1. Juice all the ingredients.
2. Add some crushed ice in 2 glasses and pour the juice over it. Serve immediately.

MIXER / BLENDER

1. Blend all the ingredients using little water (if required) till smooth.
2. Strain the juice using a strainer or a muslin cloth.
3. Add some crushed ice in 2 glasses and pour the juice over it. Serve immediately.

....

Nutritive values per glass:
Energy : 158 kcal.
Protein : 2.0 gm.
Carbohydrate : 35.3 gm.
Fat : 0.9 gm.
Fibre : 3.5 gm.
Potassium : 294.8 mg.

Apples contain pectin (a soluble fibre that helps to lower the cholesterol levels) and antioxidants (that help to get rid of the free radicals lurking in our bodies, which would otherwise deferiorate the lining of the heart). Low in calories, apple is an 'all round' fabulous fruit. Carrots too are rich in fibre that binds the bad cholesterol (LDL) and throws it out from our body. Whereas ginger imparts its flavour and a substance "gingerol" to this drink, which improves blood circulation.

~ Anti Cholesterol Shake ~

Picture on page 75.

A combination of orange, papaya and banana blended together to make a filling drink that beats cholesterol!

Makes 2 small glasses (300 ml).

Ingredients

1 medium sized orange, peeled and separated into segments
¼ medium sized papaya, peeled and cut into pieces
1 banana, peeled and cut into pieces
crushed ice to serve

Procedure

HOPPER / JUICER

1. Juice all the ingredients except bananas.
2. Blend the bananas to a purée in a blender and add to the juice.
3. Add some crushed ice in 2 glasses and pour the juice over it. Serve immediately.

MIXER / BLENDER

1. Blend all the ingredients using little water (if required) till smooth.
2. Strain the juice using a strainer or a muslin cloth.
3. Add some crushed ice in 2 glasses and pour the juice over it. Serve immediately.

....

Nutritive values per glass:
Energy : 58 kcal.
Protein : 0.8 gm.
Carbohydrate : 13.3 gm.
Fat : 0.2 gm.
Potassium : 52.2 mg.
Vitamin C : 45.4 mg.
Fibre : 1.0 gm.

This unusual combination of fruits is rich in potassium, vitamin C and fibre. Banana is an excellent source of potassium, the deficiency of which is associated with the change in the normal pattern of the heartbeat. This shake satiates the hunger pangs while keeping the building up of cholesterol levels at all time low.

~ *Lemon Pleasure* ~

A drink that helps to add taste back into the day! This great combination not only looks good, but is also a nutritious way to bring back your humour!

Makes 2 small glasses (300 ml).

Ingredients
2 large apples (unpeeled), cored and cut into pieces
1 cup black jamun, deseeded
1 tbsp lemon juice
crushed ice to serve

Procedure
MIXER / BLENDER
1. Blend all the ingredients using little water (if required) till smooth.
2. Add the lemon juice and mix well.

3. Add some crushed ice in 2 glasses and pour the juice over it. Serve immediately.

....

Nutritive values per glass:
Energy : 288 kcal.
Protein : 1.5 gm.
Carbohydrate : 65.1 gm.
Fat : 2.2 gm.
Vitamin C : 24.7 mg.
Fibre : 4.0 gm.

Soluble fibre (pectin) present in the apple skin help to keep blood sugar levels under a check. Jamun is considered as a traditional medicine that helps pancreas release insulin (a hormone that is necessary to control blood sugar levels) and control diabetes. Jamun is a good source of vitamin C and is also rich in calcium and phosphorous. Fibre being such an important nutrient for diabetics, it should be retained in the juice. Hence, enjoy this juice without straining it as shown in this recipe.

~ Veggie Boost ~

Picture on page 2.

These refreshing veggies (carrot, spinach, parsley, celery) combine to make a super juice rich in fibre to keep a check on blood sugar.

Makes 2 small glasses (300 ml).

Ingredients
4 medium sized carrots (unpeeled), cut into pieces
12 to 15 spinach (palak) leaves, roughly chopped
10 parsley stems with leaves, roughly chopped
6 celery sticks, roughly chopped
1 tbsp lemon juice
crushed ice to serve

Procedure
HOPPER / JUICER

1. Juice all the ingredients.
2. Add the lemon juice and mix well.
3. Add some crushed ice in 2 glasses and pour the juice over it. Serve immediately.

MIXER / BLENDER

1. Blend all the ingredients using little water (if required) till smooth.
2. Strain the juice using a strainer or a muslin cloth.
3. Add the lemon juice and mix well.
4. Add some crushed ice in 2 glasses and pour the juice over it. Serve immediately.

....

Nutritive values per glass:
Energy : 111 kcal.
Protein : 2.6 gm.
Carbohydrate : 23.7 gm.
Fat : 0.7 gm.
Zinc : 0.9 mg.
Potassium : 325.6 mg.
Fibre : 3.2 gm.

Carrots and spinach have been credited with zinc that aid in increasing the HDL (good cholesterol) cholesterol levels and diminishing the likelihood of blood clots and heart disease in diabetics. Being rich in potassium, this drink is a boon for diabetics with hypertension (high blood pressure) as it helps to balance the high sodium levels.

Hypertension

~ *Red Dynamo* ~

Picture on facing page.

This juice may not win a lot apprehension from friends and relatives, in which "Doctor garlic" represents the ultimate in veggie power.

Makes 2 small glasses (300 ml).

Ingredients
6 medium sized carrots (unpeeled), cut into pieces
6 celery sticks with the leaves, roughly chopped
10 parsley stems with the leaves, roughly chopped
2 pearl garlics or 2 garlic cloves
crushed ice to serve

For High Cholesterol and Hypertension : FROM LEFT TO RIGHT
POTASSIUM BROTH : Recipe on page 77, RED DYNAMO : Recipe above ↣
and ANTI CHOLESTEROL SHAKE : Recipe on page 68. ↣ 74

Procedure

HOPPER / JUICER

1. Juice all the ingredients.
2. Add some crushed ice in 2 glasses and pour the juice over it. Serve immediately.

MIXER / BLENDER

1. Blend all the ingredients using little water (if required) till smooth.
2. Strain the juice using a strainer or a muslin cloth.
3. Add some crushed ice in 2 glasses and pour the juice over it. Serve immediately.

....

Nutritive values per glass:

Energy : 148 kcal.
Protein : 2.9 gm.
Carbohydrate : 32.6 gm.
Fat : 0.6 gm.
Potassium : 356.1 mg.
Vitamin C : 15.1 mg.
Fibre : 4.0 gm.

The garlic express kick starts the immune system, detoxifies the liver and very importantly helps to lower blood pressure. A glass of this juice daily will positively endeavour to maintain normal blood pressure.

~ *Potassium Broth* ~

Picture on page 75.

This carrot and black grape combination is of an eye-pleasing magenta colour and is high in potassium.

Makes 2 small glasses (300 ml).

Ingredients
4 medium sized carrots (unpeeled), cut into pieces
½ cup black grapes
crushed ice to serve

Procedure
HOPPER / JUICER

1. Juice all the ingredients.
2. Add some crushed ice in 2 glasses and pour the juice over it. Serve immediately.

MIXER / BLENDER

1. Blend all the ingredients using little water (if required) till smooth.
2. Strain the juice using a strainer or a muslin cloth.

3. Add some crushed ice in 2 glasses and pour the juice over it. Serve immediately.

....

Nutritive values per glass:
Energy : 121 kcal.
Protein : 2.0 gm.
Carbohydrate : 27.0 gm.
Fat : 0.5 gm.
Potassium : 216.0 mg.
Zinc : 0.8 mg.
Iron : 2.2 mg.

Hypertensives will undoubtedly benefit from this healthy broth. The potassium from the carrot helps to balance the high sodium levels during hypertension thus maintaining normal blood pressure. The black grapes perk up the juice with their sweetness and lend the necessary striking colour.

~ *Spinach and Mint Juice* ~

Picture on page 2.

Here is a cool and healthy cleanser to start your day with. The lemon in this dark green juice helps to retain the colour and enhance the absorption of iron in it.

Makes 2 small glasses (300 ml).

Ingredients
25 to 30 spinach (palak) leaves
20 mint (phudina) sprigs, with the leaves
15 coriander sprigs, with the leaves
1 tsp lemon juice
1 tsp jal jeera powder (optional)
crushed ice to serve

Procedure
HOPPER / JUICER
1. Juice all the ingredients.

2. Add the lemon juice and jal jeera powder and mix well.
3. Add some crushed ice in 2 glasses and pour the juice over it. Serve immediately.

MIXER / BLENDER
1. Blend all the ingredients using little water (if required) till smooth.
2. Strain the juice using a strainer or a muslin cloth.
3. Add the lemon juice and jal jeera powder and mix well.
4. Add some crushed ice in 2 glasses and pour the juice over it. Serve immediately.

....

Nutritive values per glass:
Energy : 24 kcal.
Protein : 1.9 gm.
Carbohydrate : 3.0 gm.
Fat : 0.5 gm.
Fibre : 0.9 gm.
Iron : 3.0 mg.
Calcium : 81.2 mg.

The greens and the jal jeera powder together are ideal for stimulating the digestive system and replacing the lost minerals. Digestive oils in mint aid digestion. Take this on an empty stomach daily. Do not eat anything immediately in order to let this juice do its work and help you steer clear of indigestion.

~ *Digestive Aid* ~

Picture on page 2.

As lovely to look at as it is good for the digestive system! This eye-appealing vitality juice is made of pineapple, orange and apple.

Makes 2 small glasses (300 ml).

Ingredients
3 big pineapple slices with the skin, cut into pieces
1 big orange, peeled and separated into segments
1 medium sized apple (unpeeled), cored and cut into pieces
crushed ice to serve

Procedure
HOPPER / JUICER

1. Juice all the ingredients.
2. Add some crushed ice in 2 glasses and pour the juice over it. Serve immediately.

MIXER / BLENDER

1. Blend all the ingredients using little water (if required) till smooth.

2. Strain the juice using a strainer or a muslin cloth.
3. Add some crushed ice in 2 glasses and pour the juice over it. Serve immediately.

....

Nutritive values per glass:
Energy : 133 kcal.
Protein : 1.0 gm.
Carbohydrate : 30.6 gm.
Fat : 0.7 gm.
Fibre : 1.7 gm.
Vitamin A : 603.1 mcg.

Here's a natural indispensible solution to indigestion. The fibre from the apple and pineapple and the sharp acidity from the oranges assist in bowel movements thus relieving indigestion. To get the utmost of fibre from apples do not peel them and do not strain the juice either, since much of the fibre lies just beneath the skin.

~ *Calcium Booster* ~

Picture on back cover.

Bones form the framework your body rests on… and this drink will make sure they remain healthy and strong forever!

Makes 2 small glasses (300 ml).

Ingredients
2 small beetroots (unpeeled), cut into pieces
2 medium sized carrots (unpeeled), cut into pieces
3 to 4 parsley stems, roughly chopped
2 to 3 celery sticks, roughly chopped
crushed ice to serve

Procedure
HOPPER / JUICER

1. Juice all the ingredients.
2. Add some crushed ice in 2 glasses and pour the juice over it. Serve immediately.

MIXER / BLENDER

1. Blend all the ingredients using little water (if required) till smooth.
2. Strain the juice using a strainer or a muslin cloth.
3. Add some crushed ice in 2 glasses and pour the juice over it. Serve immediately.

....

Nutritive values per glass:
Energy : 89 kcal.
Protein : 2.6 gm.
Carbohydrate : 19.0 gm.
Fat : 0.3 gm.
Calcium : 115.5 mg.
Vitamin C : 16.0 mg.
Folic Acid : 23.3 mcg.

This juice is not only rich in calcium but also provides a treasure trove of other nutrients like vitamin C and folic acid. Carrots make sweet juice that works well as a base when combined with juice of other fruits and vegetables. It is advised to drink fresh carrot juice as it contains more easily assimilated calcium than milk.

FRESH AND FRUITY : FROM LEFT TO RIGHT
COCO PINEAPPLE DELIGHT : Recipe on page 97 and GRAPLE : Recipe on page 93.

~ *Calci Mix in a Glass* ~

Picture on back cover.

Wave goodbye to your worries of weak bones and tooth decay with this
"calcium in a glass"!

Makes 2 small glasses (300 ml).

Ingredients
2 medium sized carrots (unpeeled), cut into pieces
1 medium sized orange, peeled and separated into segments
½ medium sized apple (unpeeled), cored and cut into pieces
2 to 3 spinach (palak) leaves, roughly chopped
1 to 2 finely chopped celery sticks (with the leaves) and crushed ice to serve

Procedure
HOPPER / JUICER

1. Juice all the ingredients.
2. Add chopped celery and some crushed ice in 2 glasses and pour the juice over it. Serve immediately.

MIXER / BLENDER

1. Blend all the ingredients using little water (if required) till smooth.
2. Strain the juice using a strainer or a muslin cloth.
3. Add chopped celery and some crushed ice in 2 glasses and pour the juice over it. Serve immediately.

....

Nutritive values per glass:
Energy : 107 kcal.
Protein : 1.6 gm.
Carbohydrate : 23.8 gm.
Fat : 0.6 gm.
Calcium : 117.6 mg.
Vitamin C : 21.6 mg.

Overflowing with instantly available essential nutrients, Calci Mix provides power, energy and stamina - just in a glass. The high vitamin C content of this juice further aids in the absorption of calcium. Serve it topped with chopped celery which besides adding crunch to this drink makes it more colourful and interesting.

~ *Super 7 Stress Reliever* ~

This super 7 shot is guaranteed to chase away the blues and to put a glow back on your skin!

Makes 2 small glasses (300 ml).

Ingredients
1 medium sized carrot (unpeeled), cut into pieces
1 small beetroot (unpeeled), cut into pieces
2 medium sized tomatoes, cut into pieces
2 celery sticks, roughly chopped
3 to 4 parsley stems with the leaves, roughly chopped
2 to 3 coriander sprigs with the leaves, roughly chopped
6 to 8 spinach (palak) leaves, roughly chopped
crushed ice to serve

Procedure

HOPPER / JUICER

1. Juice all the ingredients.
2. Add some crushed ice in 2 glasses and pour the juice over it. Serve immediately.

MIXER / BLENDER

1. Blend all the ingredients using little water (if required) till smooth.
2. Strain the juice using a strainer or a muslin cloth.
3. Add some crushed ice in 2 glasses and pour the juice over it. Serve immediately.

. . . .

Nutritive values per glass:
Energy : 62 kcal.
Protein : 2.2 gm.
Carbohydrate : 12.4 gm.
Fat : 0.4 gm.
Vitamin A : 2060.0 mcg.
Vitamin C : 37.6 mg.
Vitamin E : 0.4 mg.

Besides tasting delicious, this drink works good as a stress reliever for your body as it overflows with a mass of antioxidants like vitamin A, C and E. Antioxidants engulf the free radicals that enter our body and stop their deteriorating action on healthy cells and organs. Thus preventing wrinkled skin and other diseases. Just one glass everyday will give you instant energy and high levels of immunity.

~ *Melon Magic* ~

To get your mind to start working at top speed and to get the much-needed boost of creative energy, grab a glass of this magic portion!

Makes 2 small glasses (300 ml).

Ingredients

½ small muskmelon (kharbiooja), peeled and cut into pieces
1 medium sized orange, peeled and separated into segments
1 tsp lemon juice
2 parsley stems, finely chopped and crushed ice to serve

Procedure

HOPPER / JUICER

1. Juice all the ingredients.
2. Add the lemon juice and mix well.
3. Add chopped parsley and some crushed ice in 2 glasses and pour the juice over it. Serve immediately.

MIXER / BLENDER

1. Blend all the ingredients using little water (if required) till smooth.
2. Strain the juice using a strainer or a muslin cloth.
3. Add the lemon juice and mix well.
4. Add chopped parsley and some crushed ice in a 2 glasses and pour the juice over it. Serve immediately.

....

Nutritive values per glass:
Energy : 85 kcal.
Protein : 1.4 gm.
Carbohydrate : 18.6 gm.
Fat : 0.6 gm.
Vitamin A : 1522.2 mcg.

This is an ultimate healing juice, ideal as an immune booster due to its high vitamin A levels. Vitamin A (Beta-carotene) is a potent antioxidant that delays ageing, fights cancers, promotes greater concentration and aids in mental alertness.

FRESH AND FRUITY

With the changing lifestyle one tends to choose the wide variety of readymade bottled juices and soft drinks that are easily available. These juices, though convenient and time saving, provide empty calories (high in sugar) and are devoid of many valuable nutrients.

Commercial juices are heat-treated to lengthen shelf life, which leads to loss of some of the heat labile nutrients like vitamin C and B-complex. In addition to this, the added preservatives deter the absorption of the nutrients and increase the juices' sodium content.

Homemade fruit juices on the other hand, are fresh, delicious and without any added preservatives and stabilizers. They help to cleanse the body and nourish it with important nutrients in a form that is easy to digest and absorb.

This special section on **'Fresh and Fruity'** comprises of tasty and delicious juices that are made exclusively using fresh fruits. Although any fruit can be used, juices that we have clubbed under this section are particularly healthy and delicious such as **Graple**, page 93, which is an unusual combination of sweet tasting apples and tangy grapes, **Coco Pineapple Delight**, page 97, an unique combination of cooling coconut water and fibre rich pineapple, **Fruity Express**, page 99, an energizing and refreshing juice etc.

So the next time someone asks to raise a toast, produce a glassful of lip-smacking, home-made juice… and say cheers to good health!

~ *Graple* ~

Picture on page 85.

Tangy grapes and the reliable apple make for a refreshingly cool drink. A glassful will help you fight illness and keep you energetic all through the day.

Makes 2 small glasses (300 ml).

Ingredients
1 cup green grapes
2 small apples (unpeeled), cored and cut into pieces
crushed ice to serve

Procedure
HOPPER / JUICER

1. Juice all the ingredients.
2. Add some crushed ice in 2 glasses and pour the juice over it. Serve immediately.

MIXER / BLENDER

1. Blend all the ingredients using little water (if required) till smooth.
2. Strain the juice using a strainer or a muslin cloth.
3. Add some crushed ice in 2 glasses and pour the juice over it. Serve immediately.

....

Nutritive values per glass:
Energy : 174 kcal.
Protein : 0.8 gm.
Carbohydrate : 39.7 gm.
Fat : 1.3 gm.
Fibre : 4.1 gm.
Potassium : 157.5 mg.

Apples are basically sweet and the juice of grapes is a little sour, when mixed together, they compliment each other's flavour and enhance the overall taste. Grapes are rich in antioxidants and together apples and grapes join to help clean the kidneys and liver.

~ *Golden Drink* ~

Picture on cover.

Brilliantly coloured, this drink is made by combining two very unusual fruits. The enchanting colour compliments the glorious taste of pineapple and papaya.

Makes 2 small glasses (300 ml).

Ingredients
½ small pineapple with the skin, cut into pieces
½ small papaya, peeled and cut into pieces
crushed ice to serve

Procedure
HOPPER / JUICER

1. Juice all the ingredients.
2. Add some crushed ice in 2 glasses and pour the juice over it. Serve immediately.

MIXER / BLENDER

1. Blend all the ingredients using little water (if required) till smooth.
2. Strain the juice using a strainer or a muslin cloth.

3. Add some crushed ice in 2 glasses and pour the juice over it. Serve immediately.

....

Nutritive values per glass:
Energy : 103 kcal.
Protein : 1.2 gm.
Carbohydrate : 23.8 gm.
Fat : 0.3 gm.
Vitamin A : 693.7 mcg.
Iron : 4.2 mg.
Fibre : 1.6 gm.

Loaded with vitamin A and iron, this fibre-rich juice is a health-enhancing portion. Papaya and pineapple both have digestive enzymes and help overcome constipation and indigestion. Natural sugars present in them provide energy and stamina.

~ Coco Pineapple Delight ~

Picture on page 85.

What could be more refreshing than some coconut water? With the added nutrition of pineapple, this delightful drink becomes a must-have.

Makes 2 small glasses (300 ml).

Ingredients
3 big slices of pineapple with the skin, cut into pieces
1 small tender coconut (coconut water)
½ cup tender coconut meat (nariyal ki malai)

Procedure
HOPPER / JUICER

1. Juice the pineapple slices.
2. Chop the tender coconut meat finely.
3. Mix together the pineapple juice, tender coconut meat and tender coconut water.
4. Add some crushed ice in 2 glasses and pour the juice over it. Serve immediately.

MIXER / BLENDER

1. Blend all the ingredients till smooth.
2. Add some crushed ice in 2 glasses and pour the juice over it. Serve immediately.

....

Nutritive values per glass:
Energy : 76 kcal.
Protein : 1.3 gm.
Carbohydrate : 15.9 gm.
Fat : 0.8 gm.
Potassium : 224.5 mg.
Vitamin C : 31.8 mg.

A mind-blowing combination of pineapple and coconut meat, added to the wholesome coconut water! Coconut is rich in potassium and pineapple in vitamin C. Enzyme 'bromelin' in pineapple helps stabilize the acid-alkaline balance of body fluids and improves digestion.

~ *Fruity Express* ~

A glass of energy for your little darlings to keep them pepped throughout the day!

Makes 2 small glasses (300 ml).

Ingredients
¼ medium sized muskmelon (kharbooja), peeled and cut into slices
1 medium sized apple (unpeeled), cored and cut into pieces
¼ cup green grapes
1 tsp lemon juice
crushed ice to serve

Procedure
HOPPER / JUICER

1. Juice all the ingredients.
2. Add the lemon juice and mix well.
3. Add some crushed ice in 2 glasses and pour the juice over it. Serve immediately.

MIXER / BLENDER

1. Blend all the ingredients using little water (if required) till smooth.
2. Strain the juice using a strainer or a muslin cloth.
3. Add the lemon juice and mix well.
4. Add some crushed ice in 2 glasses and pour the juice over it. Serve immediately.

....

Nutritive values per glass:
Energy : 83 kcal.
Protein : 0.5 gm.
Carbohydrate : 18.8 gm.
Fat : 0.7 gm.
Fibre : 1.8 gm.
Vitamin C : 13.5 mg.

Kids are more open to drinking juices than they are to eating whole fruits. This great new blend is an easy way to get them to down some a nutri-mix. Most fruits are available the year around, the seasonal ones can be replaced by the ones of your choice.

~ *Tangy Twist* ~

Picture on cover.

This great juice with the tangy twist of orange is great at any time of the day.

Makes 2 small glasses (300 ml).

Ingredients
2 small oranges, peeled and separated into segments
½ cup pomegranate (anar)
½ cup black grapes
crushed ice to serve

Procedure
HOPPER / JUICER

1. Juice all the ingredients.
2. Add some crushed ice in 2 glasses and pour the juice over it. Serve immediately.

MIXER / BLENDER

1. Blend all the ingredients using little water (if required) till smooth.
2. Strain the juice using a strainer or a muslin cloth.
3. Add some crushed ice in 2 glasses and pour the juice over it. Serve immediately.

....

Nutritive values per glass:
Energy : 99 kcal.
Protein : 1.5 gm.
Carbohydrate : 22.5 gm.
Fat : 0.4 gm.
Vitamin A : 1170.2 mcg.
Vitamin C : 37.9 mg.

Pretty pearls of health... that's what pomegranates are best known as, because of their vitamin C, potassium and fibre content. Sometimes difficult to find, pomegranates are worth buying when you see them because their exotic and distinctive flavour is quite delicious. A reddish skin is usually a sign that the seeds inside will be vibrant and sweet.

Total Health Series by Tarla Dalal

The Total Health series is a range of cookbooks specially designed and carefully researched by a team of qualified nutritionists. These books are an action-oriented guide for good health and wellness to suit the nutritional needs for different age groups, be it an expectant mum, a baby, an individual who has a medical problem or aims to lose weight. These books will help you and your family stay in fine fettle. They have opened new vistas in the field of cooking while providing you with healthy guidelines for adding verve and vitality to your life. Some of the titles in this series are:

**Low Calorie
Healthy Cooking**

Pregnancy Cook Book

**Baby & Toddler
Cook Book**

**Healthy Heart
Cook Book**